Jim and Jam
and the Builders

this is
Jim

in every picture
look for his pet mouse
Jam

Written and devised by Angela Littler
Illustrated by Anita McEwen

HODDER AND STOUGHTON
LONDON   SYDNEY   AUCKLAND   TORONTO

Jim likes to go
to the building site.
He helps the builders.
Jam goes with him.
But Jam does not help.

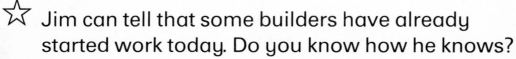

☆ Jim can tell that some builders have already
started work today. Do you know how he knows?

- How many builders are on the site so far?
- Where are they?

Jim looks for Bob, the foreman.

He is a good friend.

He shows Jim

how houses are made.

Jim learns a lot.

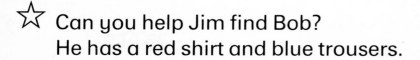
☆ Can you help Jim find Bob?
He has a red shirt and blue trousers.

- Can you find all five builders?
- How many men have yellow hats?
- How many men have red hats?

Jim puts on his hard hat.
He must be careful on the site.
Jam is not very careful,
and he has no hard hat.
Quick, Jim! Catch Jam!

☆ Some of the pipes are jumbled up. There are
five short ones and four long ones.
Can you find them?

- The builders' names are Alf, Bob, Colin, Don and Ed. They have their initials on their hats. Can you tell who's who?

No-one can catch
the little mouse.
He can hide in tiny places.
Everyone is in a mess.
Come here, Jam!

☆ Four of the men have lost their boots while
chasing Jam over the wet cement. Can you help
to find them?

● How many dirty socks can you see?

Look out! Danger!

The pipes are falling down.

They will hurt someone.

Bob has an idea.

He runs to the dumper truck.

 The lorry has just brought more paint for the houses. Which tins belong to which house?

● How many tins of paint does each house get?

Hooray!

Bob has saved the day.

Jam finds a safe place to sit.

He does not want

to play on a building site again.

 Bob has knocked over the door and window
frames. How many are there of each?

● Can you spot four triangle shapes among
the frames?

Everyone has lunch.

They have sandwiches and fruit.

Bob reads a newspaper.

The others listen to the radio.

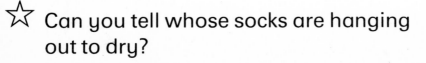

☆ Can you tell whose socks are hanging
out to dry?

- What shapes are the men's sandwiches?
- Which builder owns which lunch box?
- Who owns the unopened lunch box?

The men get back to work.
Jim and Jam go home.
Next time Jim comes
he will leave Jam at home.
Goodbye Jim! Goodbye Jam!

☆ One of the gasman's pipes has a break in it,
so one house will get no gas. Can you tell
which one?

- If you could work on a building site
what job would you like?

Word and Picture Puzzle

 house

 digger

 spade.

 door

 dumper

 bricks

 window

 mixer

 sandwich

 pipe

wheel barrow

 hard hat

Look at these pictures and read the words several times.
Try putting a strip of paper (or a coin, or your hand)
over the pictures. Now can you read what each word says?

Demolition Skittles

You can play this game alone or with friends. Scrunch up some newspaper into a big ball, and fasten it tight with sticky tape. Tie a piece of string around the ball.

Now set out six tall cardboard tubes in a triangle shape. You can decorate the tubes to look like houses. Now you are ready to play.

Swing the demolition ball, and try to knock down all six skittles in one go. The person who knocks down most skittles is the winner.

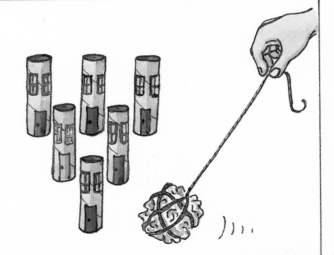

Make a Dumper

You will need

scissors

sticky tape

square box for cab

ruler

children's glue

large cereal box

smaller cereal box

lots of toilet roll tubes

Ask a grown-up to help you with this. You can carry loads of pipes in your dumper and deliver them wherever you want. Remember – do not use heavy things for the load (cardboard tubes are best).

four tops for wheels

1

Stick the wheels on either side of the big cereal box with children's glue.

2

Cut one big side and the end off the small cereal box.

3

Fix the small box onto the large one *at the back only*, with sticky tape.

4

Cut windows in the square box and stick it onto the base to make a cab. Fill the dumper with cardboard "pipes".

5

Place a ruler part way under the dumper (see the picture at the top of the page). Bang your fist sharply down on the other end of the ruler, and dump your load of pipes. Happy dumping!

Bricklayer's Game

A game for two people. You will need a dice and two counters. Start at the bottom, one person on each side, and take turns to throw the dice and move your counters up the brick steps. If you land on a brick that has something on it, then you must go back to the beginning. If you throw a six, you have an extra turn. First one to the top gets the delicious hamburger for lunch!

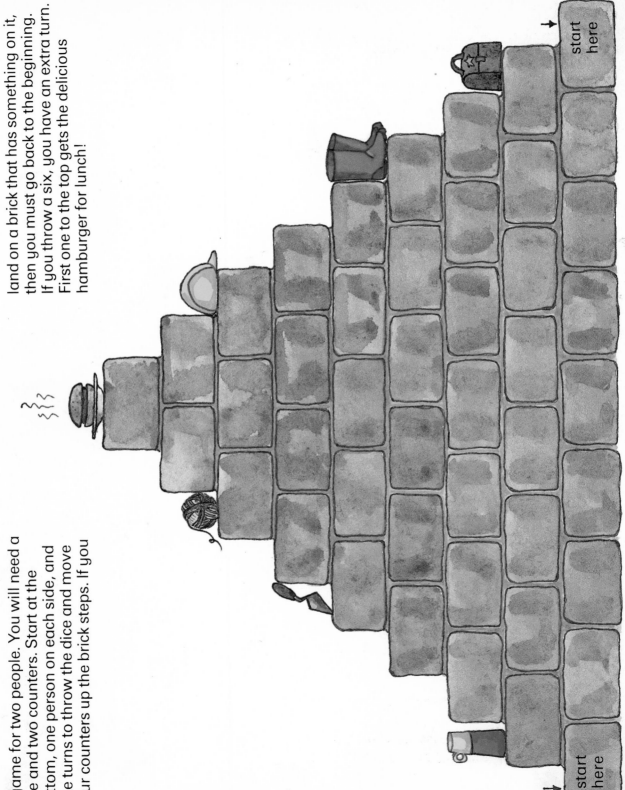

start here

start here